INTERESTING TIMES

Peter Brookes

Biteback Publishing

For our grandson, Kit

First published in Great Britain in 2017 by
Biteback Publishing Ltd
Westminster Tower
3 Albert Embankment
London SE1 7SP
Copyright © Peter Brookes 2017

ISBN 978-1-78590-253-6

10 9 8 7 6 5 4 3 2 1

A CIP catalogue record for this book is available from the British Library.

Printed and bound in Great Britain by
CPI Group (UK) Ltd, Croydon CR0 4YY

MIX
Paper from
responsible sources
FSC
www.fsc.org   FSC® C020471

INTRODUCTION

By Peter Brookes

'May you live in interesting times' is an (apocryphal) Chinese curse, delivered ironically. Only in uninteresting times, it suggests, can we flourish. We are indeed cursed, then, because these past two years have seen political and social upheaval not matched in my lifetime. Trump, Corbyn, Brexit, May, Macron have all defied prediction. Terrorism here finds ever more gruesome forms, be it Islamist or white supremacist. Social cohesion immolates in a tower block inferno.

It's a sad business to think that political cartoonists benefit professionally from all of this, but the greater the chaos, the richer our material. The more the world suffers, the more impelled are we to put it down on paper, fuelled either by anger or by a sense of ridicule. The worse it is for everyone else, the better the adrenalin flows.

Who could have imagined two years ago that Washington and Westminster would be ruled by orange men? The emergence of Donald J. Trump, though, has not brought unalloyed joy to my working life, despite people remarking that 'you must be so glad to have such great subject matter'. For sure, he's a treat to draw with that ridiculous hair, the florid complexion with white circles round the eyes (presumably caused by the sun bed), the pout, the expanse of rolling flesh, those gestures made with tiny hands, only just sticking out from the arms of his voluminous suits. And those ties! Soooooo long. Ah, yes, Trumpspeak! This is a gift for captions, when everything is repeated and every other word is 'beautiful'. The problem is that it is increasingly difficult to make a joke of a joke. He is held in such universal opprobrium that I feel I'm preaching to the converted all the time. Perhaps he has too quickly become an easy target, though always an enjoyable one.

The same could be said of Boris and Michael Gove. They have always been seen as a bit of a joke, but because they are both so toxic I never feel the need to let up on them. How could one resist drawing that bumbling, overweight, blond Eton mess whenever he puts his foot in it, which is often? Or Gove, with cartoon lips to die for and those heavy, swotty specs? In fact, they were made for each other, and gave me perhaps my cartooning highlight of this collection. It was immediately after the referendum, in the unseemly scramble for the Tory leadership after Cameron's abject resignation. Govey viciously stabbed Boris in the back in order to seize the crown for himself, but I show the blade carrying through to stab the treacherous swine in the front. It was high political drama, and I can remember watching the unfolding events in absolute disbelief. You couldn't make it up, and I didn't need to as the metaphor was handed to me on a plate.

These instances, when you have to react to momentous events with great speed while the clock ticks and your deadline is horrifyingly close, are for me the very stuff of cartooning. The adrenalin is pumping, it's panic stations, and you're not at all sure if you're going to fall flat on your face or not. The nature of the event can of course make things more difficult. What if you have to deal not with a political metaphor but with real violence? If it is an atrocity (the Manchester Arena bombing, the London terror attacks, Jo Cox's murder), then the stakes are somehow much higher, because one has to deal with the 'what on earth can I draw in the face of THAT?' factor. One always comes up with something on these occasions, but one often wishes it were less inadequate.

The Corbyn phenomena, the change from no-hoper to credible challenger for No. 10, hasn't really altered the way I view him. For a start, I still don't believe the nation would be stupid enough to elect him, although they were with Brexit, so who knows? It's the sheer mendacity of the man (mind you, Theresa May is no more truthful), and of those around him, that gets me. Pretending to be a Remainer, when historically an out-and-out Leaver; knowing that his support for the IRA and other terror factions is probably beyond the memory of most voters; letting sidekicks like McDonnell stir up the mob while he stands on dignity. So there he now is, smarter in suits and ties than in the rumpled beige jackets he wore when first elected leader, with pens in the top pocket like a woodwork teacher. But what the hell, that's how I still draw him, always with his Lenin cap, and one manic eye larger than the other. And, of course, beards are always a good look for a revolutionary.

Theresa May, I thought, would be problematic. Yes, we'd drawn her many times as Home Secretary, but the more searching spotlight shone on the Prime Minister has revealed a charisma-free zone. So not a lot to go on there. Women politicians are notoriously difficult to draw (perhaps we hold back a little), but luckily she gives plenty of ammunition. The distinctive nose, large bags under shifty eyes, the stoop, the dome of grey/white hair and of course those shoes. No need to draw any more than these leopard prints, and you'd know who it was meant to be. But add the too-short split skirts and the OTT necklaces, and the picture is complete. Before the disastrous snap election of 2017, she appeared unassailable – strong and stable, to coin a phrase. But now she is weak, and her starchy, humourless persona is much more vulnerable to ridicule. When a politician who takes herself so seriously is laughed at, she is finished. The fact that she now heads a minority government, propped up on occasion by the appalling DUP, as she struggles to deliver the Brexit she wants, has just made these times a lot, lot more interesting.

Young Syrian asylum seeker Alan Kurdi is found drowned attempting to reach the Greek island of Kos.

4 ix 15

Jeremy Corbyn's first PMQs as Leader of the Opposition.

Corbyn reiterates his support for a united Ireland.

Ten people are killed in a mass shooting at a community college in Oregon, the USA's 45th school shooting in 2015.

Labour deputy leader Tom Watson is accused of making unfounded allegations after police drop rape inquiry against former Home Secretary Leon Brittan.

More than 300 lawyers sign an open letter criticising the government's
'deeply inadequate' response to the Syrian migrant crisis.

Nicola Sturgeon pitches the SNP as 'the only effective opposition' to David Cameron's government at the SNP conference in Aberdeen.

Britain agrees £40 billion worth of deals with China during President Xi Jinping's state visit.

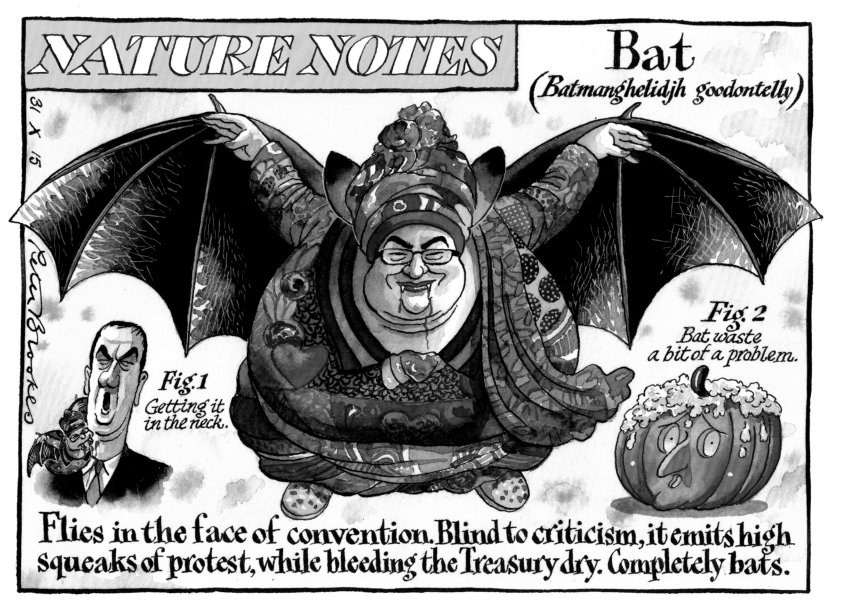

Camila Batmanghelidjh faces continuing questions over Kids Company's use of government grants.

Jeremy Corbyn is challenged by Labour MPs over his stance on the shoot-to-kill policy against terrorists.

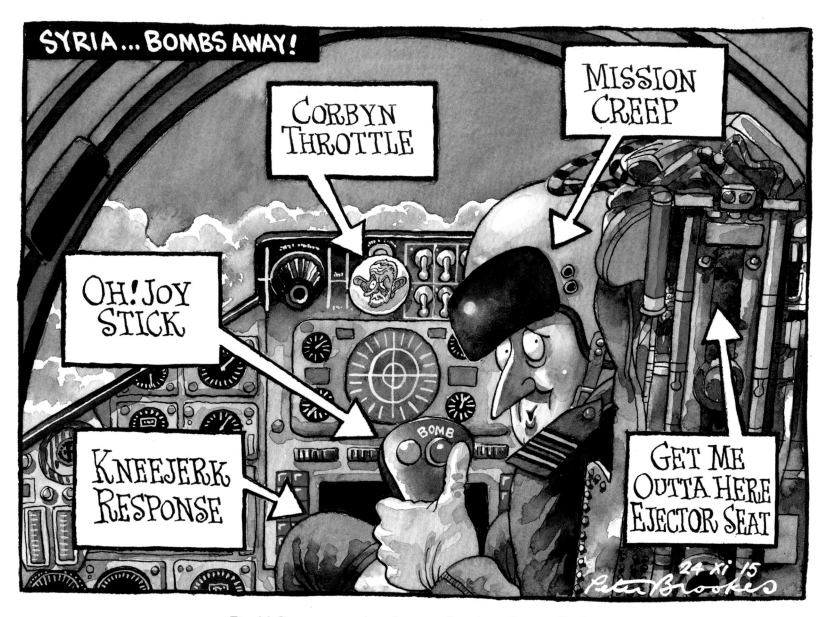

David Cameron makes the case for air strikes on Syria.

Saudi Arabia plans to execute more than fifty people convicted of terrorism-related charges.

Jeremy Corbyn celebrates Labour's victory in the Oldham by-election.

The Hatton Garden jewellery heist gang are convicted, while Jeremy Corbyn celebrates a surge in Labour's membership.

David Cameron condemns the segregation of Muslim women in British society.

As frustration mounts at the lack of diversity among the Oscar nominees, Donald
Trump's momentum shows no sign of slowing in his presidential bid.

David Cameron seeks a 'new settlement' for Britain in Europe.

Google's deal to pay back £130 million in taxes is widely condemned as 'derisory'.

Trump is mocked by his Republican rivals for skipping a presidential debate.

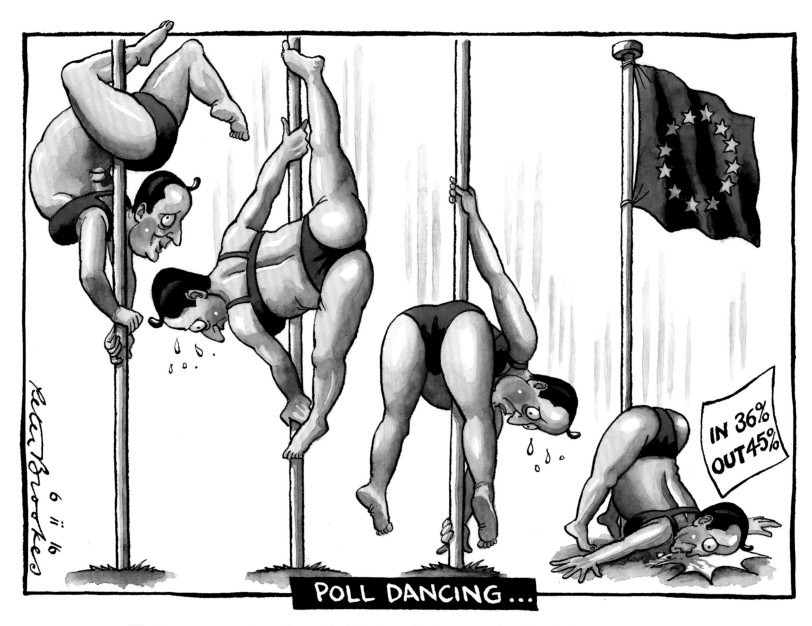

POLL DANCING...

The Leave campaign takes a lead in the polls four months ahead of the Brexit vote.

North Korea fires a long-range missile.

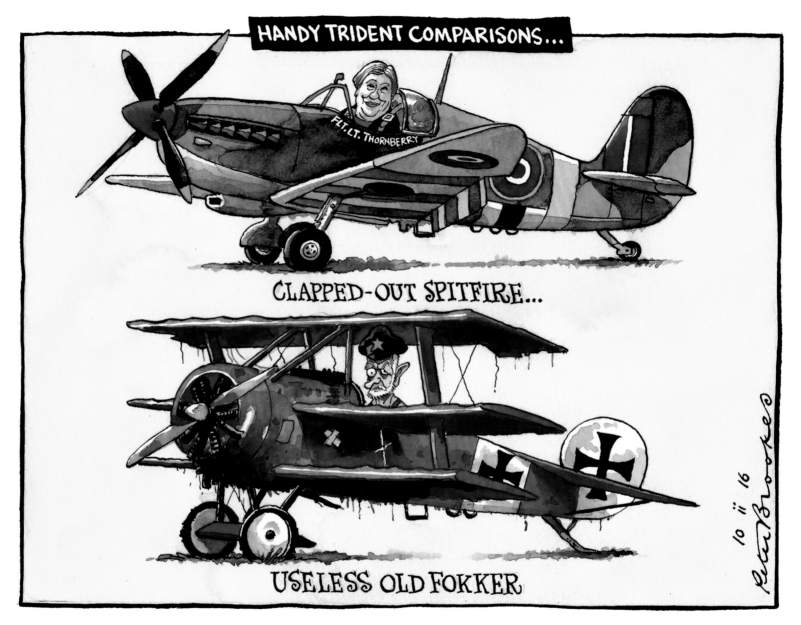

Shadow Defence Secretary Emily Thornberry claims Trident could soon be as obsolete as the Spitfire.

Donald Trump secures a convincing victory in New Hampshire's Republican primary.

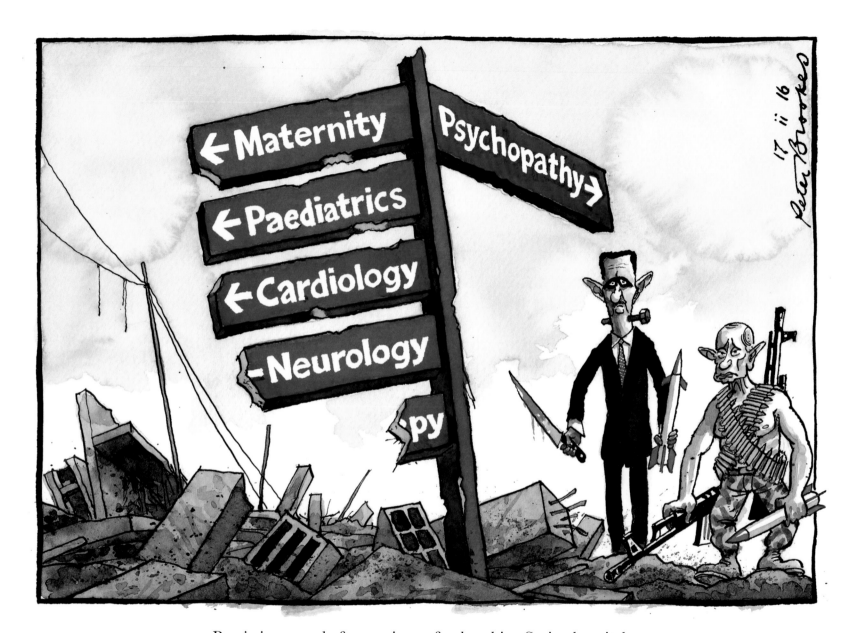

Russia is accused of war crimes after bombing Syrian hospitals.

Boris Johnson says Cameron must do more to convince him to support the Remain campaign.

David Cameron is reportedly furious after Michael Gove breaks a
promise to keep a low profile in the Brexit campaign.

Chancellor George Osborne suffers a backlash over plans for welfare budget cuts.

Nigel Farage voices his hopes that Boris Johnson will join the Leave campaign.

David Cameron defends spending £9 million on a government-produced pro-EU leaflet.

David Cameron says wealth is 'not a dirty word' following the Panama Papers tax row.

Rumours abound of a celebrity injunction on an extramarital threesome. Meanwhile, Paddy Ashdown, David Cameron and Neil Kinnock join forces in a cross-party phone campaign for Britain Stronger In Europe.

Donald Trump declares himself the Republican 'presumptive nominee' after victories in five north-eastern primaries.

Ken Livingstone is suspended from the Labour Party after defending
MP Naz Shah over accusations of anti-Semitism.

Labour 'hang on' after a mixed result in the local elections.

The NHS posts a record deficit of £2.45 billion.

Boris Johnson pledges to end 'open-door' immigration if Britain leaves the EU.

Jeremy Corbyn says there is 'an overwhelming case' for remaining in the EU while calling for reform.

Hillary Clinton declares herself the Democratic nominee while Bernie Sanders vows to fight on.

Prince Philip celebrates his 95th birthday as the migrant crisis continues.

Senior Tories warn of enduring scars from 'blue-on-blue' fighting in the EU referendum.

Far-right populist politicians rally around the Leave campaign in the final days before the EU referendum.

The day of the Brexit vote dawns.

TOIL AND TROUBLE...

Michael Gove, Boris Johnson and Nigel Farage get their result while David Cameron and George Osborne resign.

THE LAST SUPPER...

David Cameron briefs EU leaders on the referendum result at a summit in Brussels.

44

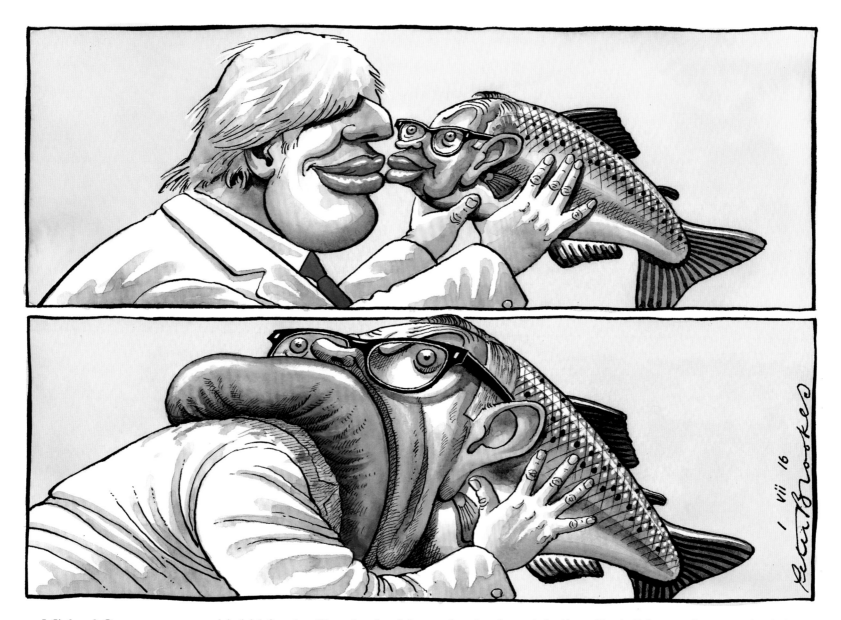

Michael Gove announces his bid for the Tory leadership, saying he doesn't believe Boris Johnson is up to the job.

The contest for Conservative leadership commences, with Liam Fox, Theresa May, Michael Gove, Stephen Crabb and Andrea Leadsom in the ring.

Michael Gove is eliminated from the Tory leadership race, with supporters
blaming his 'betrayal' of Boris Johnson for his defeat.

Five police officers are shot dead in Dallas by a lone gunman.

Theresa May wins the Conservative leadership as her final rival quits the race.

Theresa May appoints Boris Johnson as Foreign Secretary and sacks Michael Gove in her first Cabinet reshuffle.

Theresa May delays a decision on a proposed nuclear plant at Hinkley Point.

May says she is under no obligation to consult Parliament before triggering Article 50. Actor Gene Wilder dies.

Keith Vaz steps down as chairman of the Home Affairs Select Committee
following allegations over sex workers and drug use.

The government unveils plans to end the ban on grammar schools.

President Bashar al-Assad's troops launch ferocious assaults on Aleppo,
leaving nearly two million Syrian civilians without water.

'KILLER CLOWNS' TERRORISE BRITAIN...

As a 'killer clown' craze sweeps the UK, Chancellor Philip Hammond raises
concerns about the 'aggressive' behaviour of his Cabinet colleagues.

Marmite stocks run low in UK stores amid a price war sparked by the falling pound.

Trump puts on an aggressive performance in a presidential debate following allegations of sexual misconduct.

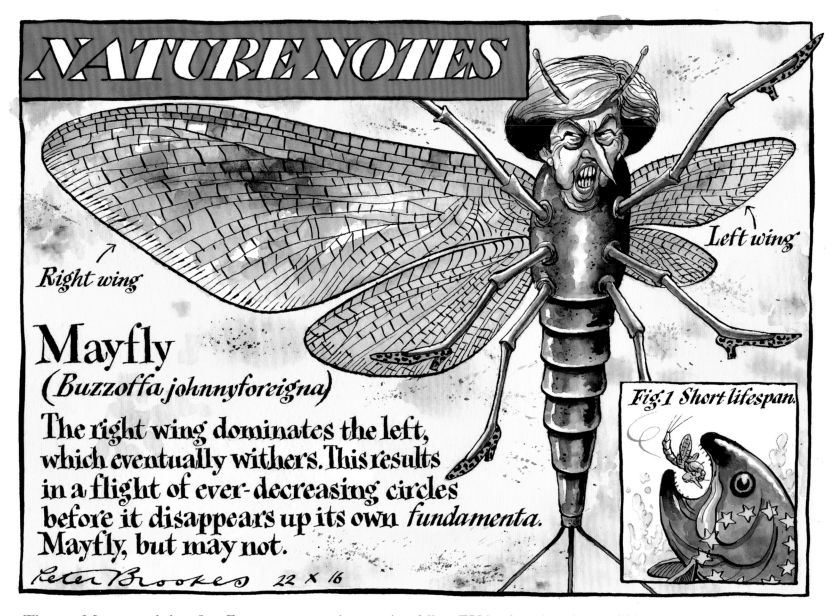

Theresa May attends her first European summit, warning fellow EU leaders that there will be no second referendum.

Donald Trump emerges as the winner of the US presidential election.

President-elect Trump visits President Obama at the White House amid speculation of Russian interference in the election result.

NATURE NOTES

Peacock
(Blairus godspareus)

All eyes on him

Fig.1
Egg
(by Fabergé)

It craves attention, strutting its arrogant stuff on the lawns of wealthy men (*cf. Kazakhstan*), where it feathers its own nest. Its cry is a piercing screech of 'me-me-me'.

26 xi 16
Peter Brookes

Tony Blair re-enters the political fray, arguing that the Brexit vote could be overturned.

YONDER STAR OVER ALEPPO...

Syrian government forces continue their assault on rebel-held eastern Aleppo, backed by Russia and Iran.

Theresa May seeks to develop post-Brexit trade links on a visit to Gulf leaders.

Time magazine names Donald Trump its Person of the Year.

Theresa May distances herself from Boris Johnson's comments about
Saudi Arabia waging 'proxy wars' across the Middle East.

THE WEST WING...

Trump's nomination of Rex Tillerson as Secretary of State sparks fresh concerns about his links with Moscow.

Berlin mourns after a truck is deliberately driven into a crowded
Christmas market, killing twelve and injuring forty-nine.

Theresa May and Boris Johnson make a song and dance about Brexit, as voting gets underway for the Oscars.

Tristram Hunt steps down as Labour MP for Stoke-on-Trent Central to become the new director of the V&A.

Theresa May outlines plans for a clean break from the EU, including leaving the single market.

Boris Johnson compares French President François Hollande to a PoW camp guard administering 'punishment beatings' to escapees 'in the manner of some WW2 movie'.

Senior Tories and prominent Brexiteers hail Trump's inauguration, amid hopes of a post-Brexit trade deal.

Donald Trump sworn in as the 45th President of the United States.

The Supreme Court rules that Parliament must be given a vote before Article 50 is triggered.

Donald Trump begins a crackdown on immigration, including building a
border wall with Mexico and blocking Syrian refugees.

Theresa May faces pressure to publicly oppose Trump's assertion that torture is effective.

MPs vote to trigger Article 50, beginning the Brexit process, at second reading.

Donald Trump's brash phone manner comes under the spotlight following leaked transcripts of his calls with Mexican President Enrique Peña Nieto and Australian Prime Minister Malcolm Turnbull.

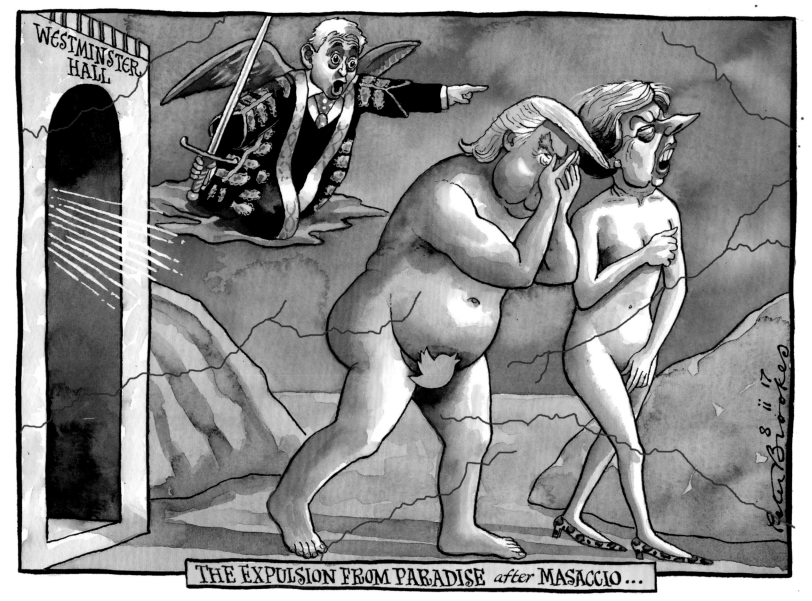

THE EXPULSION FROM PARADISE *after* MASACCIO...

House of Commons Speaker John Bercow voices strong opposition to President Trump addressing the Houses of Parliament during his proposed state visit to the UK.

The government's Brexit Bill passes in the Commons as Theresa May
warns Britain would be poorer without EU workers.

The government announces an end to the Dubs scheme, which allowed
unaccompanied child refugees to enter the UK.

The Church of England votes against a report urging continued opposition to same-sex marriage.

Following the abrupt departure of three key aides, Donald Trump
vigorously rebuts claims that his administration is in chaos.

Goalkeeper Wayne Shaw loses his job after a pie-eating promotional stunt sparks allegations of bet-fixing.

Chancellor Philip Hammond's first Budget includes a controversial rise in
National Insurance contributions for the self-employed.

Former Chancellor George Osborne is appointed the new editor of the *London Evening Standard*.

PEACEMAKER...

Former IRA leader turned deputy First Minister of Northern Ireland Martin McGuinness dies.

Khalid Masood ploughs a car into pedestrians on Westminster Bridge, killing multiple people, before fatally stabbing PC Keith Palmer.

HISTORIC AUTOGRAPHS: WHAT THEY COST YOU...

Theresa May officially triggers Article 50, amid speculation that the Brexit 'divorce bill' will cost the UK £50 billion.

Boris Johnson fails to secure G7 backing for sanctions against Russia and Syria;
elsewhere, a passenger is dragged from an overbooked United Airlines flight.

Donald Trump threatens North Korea with military action over its weapons
tests, while Kim Jong-un warns the US against provocation.

Theresa May calls for a snap general election days after referendum victory garners
Turkish President Recep Tayyip Erdoğan even greater powers.

Theresa May warns of a 'coalition of chaos' if voters opt for opposition parties.

Lib Dem leader Tim Farron faces pressure to clarify his views on homosexuality.

Diane Abbott struggles with the figures for Labour's manifesto pledge to introduce 10,000 extra police officers.

LE DÉJEUNER du BREXIT d'après Manet.

Reports emerge of a frosty dinner between EU Commission President Jean-Claude
Juncker and Theresa May before the launch of official Brexit talks.

Pope Francis looks uncomfortable during Vatican meeting with Donald Trump.

Theresa May accuses Jeremy Corbyn of using the Manchester terror attack
for political gain, while raising the UK threat level to 'critical'.

Theresa May faces heavy criticism for refusing to participate in election debates.

Donald Trump takes to Twitter to berate London Mayor Sadiq Khan for reassuring Londoners following the London Bridge terror attacks.

Theresa May delivers an unruffled victory speech after losing the Conservative majority in the general election.

Theresa May enters talks with Arlene Foster to form a minority government backed by the DUP.

A devastating fire in Grenfell Tower kills more than eighty people.

Theresa May is criticised for not meeting victims of the Grenfell Tower blaze in the immediate wake of the tragedy.

Jeremy Corbyn speaks to cheering crowds at Glastonbury Festival while Theresa
May deals with the aftermath of her disastrous election result.

Theresa May defends spending £1 billion on a deal with the DUP shortly
after claiming there is 'no magic money tree' for NHS pay.

Hurricane Irma, described by Donald Trump as 'of epic proportion', draws
attention to the President's stance on climate change.